THE TOTTERINGS' DIARY 2015

I really need a day between Saturday and Sunday...

ANNIE TEMPEST

FRANCES LINCOLN LIMITED
PUBLISHERS

Frances Lincoln Limited
www.franceslincoln.com

The Totterings' Diary 2015
Text copyright © Annie Tempest 2014
Illustrations copyright © Annie Tempest 2014

Illustrations archived and compiled by
Raymond O'Shea

Every effort is made to ensure dates are correct at the time of
going to press but the Publisher cannot accept liability for any
errors or changes.

A catalogue record for this book is available from the British Library.

ISBN 978-0-7112-3532-8

Printed in China
Bound for North Pimmshire

9 8 7 6 5 4 3 2 1

Also available from Frances Lincoln at www.franceslincoln.com
Out and About with the Totterings
Drinks with the Totterings
In the Garden with the Totterings
She Talks Venus He Talks Mars
Tottering Life
Tails of Tottering Hall
Lord Tottering: An English Gentleman
Tottering-by-Gently The First 20 Years

To find out more about the full range of Tottering-by-Gently licensed
product Telephone +44 (0)1732 866 041 or visit the Tottering-by-Gently
website at: www.tottering.com

To view or buy Annie Tempest's original watercolours visit the
O'Shea Gallery website at: www.osheagallery.com

CALENDAR 2015

JANUARY	FEBRUARY	MARCH	APRIL	MAY	JUNE
M T W T F S S	M T W T F S S	M T W T F S S	M T W T F S S	M T W T F S S	M T W T F S S

1 2 3 4	1	1	1 2 3 4 5	1 2 3	1 2 3 4 5 6 7
5 6 7 8 9 10 11	2 3 4 5 6 7 8	2 3 4 5 6 7 8	6 7 8 9 10 11 12	4 5 6 7 8 9 10	8 9 10 11 12 13 14
12 13 14 15 16 17 18	9 10 11 12 13 14 15	9 10 11 12 13 14 15	13 14 15 16 17 18 19	11 12 13 14 15 16 17	15 16 17 18 19 20 21
19 20 21 22 23 24 25	16 17 18 19 20 21 22	16 17 18 19 20 21 22	20 21 22 23 24 25 26	18 19 20 21 22 23 24	22 23 24 25 26 27 28
26 27 28 29 30 31	23 24 25 26 27 28	23 24 25 26 27 28 29	27 28 29 30	25 26 27 28 29 30 31	29 30
		30 31			

JULY	AUGUST	SEPTEMBER	OCTOBER	NOVEMBER	DECEMBER
M T W T F S S	M T W T F S S	M T W T F S S	M T W T F S S	M T W T F S S	M T W T F S S

1 2 3 4 5	1 2	1 2 3 4 5 6	1 2 3 4	1	1 2 3 4 5 6
6 7 8 9 10 11 12	3 4 5 6 7 8 9	7 8 9 10 11 12 13	5 6 7 8 9 10 11	2 3 4 5 6 7 8	7 8 9 10 11 12 13
13 14 15 16 17 18 19	10 11 12 13 14 15 16	14 15 16 17 18 19 20	12 13 14 15 16 17 18	9 10 11 12 13 14 15	14 15 16 17 18 19 20
20 21 22 23 24 25 26	17 18 19 20 21 22 23	21 22 23 24 25 26 27	19 20 21 22 23 24 25	16 17 18 19 20 21 22	21 22 23 24 25 26 27
27 28 29 30 31	24 25 26 27 28 29 30	28 29 30	26 27 28 29 30 31	23 24 25 26 27 28 29	28 29 30 31
	31			30	

CALENDAR 2016

JANUARY	FEBRUARY	MARCH	APRIL	MAY	JUNE
M T W T F S S	M T W T F S S	M T W T F S S	M T W T F S S	M T W T F S S	M T W T F S S

1 2 3	1 2 3 4 5 6 7	1 2 3 4 5 6	1 2 3	1	1 2 3 4 5
4 5 6 7 8 9 10	8 9 10 11 12 13 14	7 8 9 10 11 12 13	4 5 6 7 8 9 10	2 3 4 5 6 7 8	6 7 8 9 10 11 12
11 12 13 14 15 16 17	15 16 17 18 19 20 21	14 15 16 17 18 19 20	11 12 13 14 15 16 17	9 10 11 12 13 14 15	13 14 15 16 17 18 19
18 19 20 21 22 23 24	22 23 24 25 26 27 28	21 22 23 24 25 26 27	18 19 20 21 22 23 24	16 17 18 19 20 21 22	20 21 22 23 24 25 26
25 26 27 28 29 30 31	29	28 29 30 31	25 26 27 28 29 30	23 24 25 26 27 28 29	27 28 29 30
				30 31	

JULY	AUGUST	SEPTEMBER	OCTOBER	NOVEMBER	DECEMBER
M T W T F S S	M T W T F S S	M T W T F S S	M T W T F S S	M T W T F S S	M T W T F S S

1 2 3	1 2 3 4 5 6 7	1 2 3 4	1 2	1 2 3 4 5 6	1 2 3 4
4 5 6 7 8 9 10	8 9 10 11 12 13 14	5 6 7 8 9 10 11	3 4 5 6 7 8 9	7 8 9 10 11 12 13	5 6 7 8 9 10 11
11 12 13 14 15 16 17	15 16 17 18 19 20 21	12 13 14 15 16 17 18	10 11 12 13 14 15 16	14 15 16 17 18 19 20	12 13 14 15 16 17 18
18 19 20 21 22 23 24	22 23 24 25 26 27 28	19 20 21 22 23 24 25	17 18 19 20 21 22 23	21 22 23 24 25 26 27	19 20 21 22 23 24 25
25 26 27 28 29 30 31	29 30 31	26 27 28 29 30	24 25 26 27 28 29 30	28 29 30	26 27 28 29 30 31
			31		

THE O'SHEA GALLERY

Raymond O'Shea of The O'Shea Gallery was originally one of London's leading antiquarian print and map dealers. Historically, antiquarian galleries sponsored and promoted contemporary artists who they felt complemented their recognized areas of specialization. It was in this tradition that O'Shea first contacted *Country Life* magazine to see if Annie Tempest would like to be represented and sponsored by his gallery. In 1995 Raymond was appointed agent for Annie Tempest's originals and publisher of her books. Raymond is responsible for creating an archive of all of Annie's cartoons.

In 2003, the antiquarian side of his business was put on hold and the St. James's Street premises were finally converted to The Tottering Drawing Room at The O'Shea Gallery. It became the flagship of a worldwide operation that syndicated and licensed illustrated books, prints, stationery, champagne, jigsaws, greetings cards, ties and much more. It even launched its own fashion range of tweeds and shooting accessories under the label Gently Ltd.

In 2013 the lease on the St. James's gallery expired and Raymond O'Shea decided to take 'The Totterings on Tour'. To see the list of Tottering shows and events and the full range of Tottering product visit our website www.tottering.com. To view a large selection of Annie Tempest's Tottering-by-Gently original watercolours visit www.osheagallery.com. For any further enquiries please contact us on: +44 (0)1732 866 041.

Lord Tottering
'Dicky'

Lady Tottering
'Daffy'

Serena

Freddy

Daisy

Gladys Shagpile

Slobber

Scribble

Slobber

TOTTERING-BY-GENTLY ®
ANNIE TEMPEST

Annie Tempest is one of the top cartoonists working in the UK. This was recognized in 2009 with the Cartoon Art Trust awarding her the Pont Prize for the portrayal of the British Character. Annie's cartoon career began in 1985 with the success of her first book, *How Green Are Your Wellies?* This led to a regular cartoon, 'Westenders' in the *Daily Express*. Soon after, she joined the *Daily Mail* with 'The Yuppies' cartoon strip which ran for more than seven years and for which, in 1989, she was awarded 'Strip Cartoonist of the Year'. Since 1993 Annie Tempest has been charting the life of Daffy and Dicky Tottering in Tottering-by-Gently – the phenomenally successful weekly strip cartoon in *Country Life*.

Daffy Tottering is a woman of a certain age who has been taken into the hearts of people all over the world. She reflects the problems facing women in their everyday life and is completely at one with herself, while reflecting on the intergenerational tensions and the differing perspectives of men and women, as well as dieting, ageing, gardening, fashion, food, field sports, convention and much more.

Daffy and her husband Dicky live in the fading grandeur of Tottering Hall, their stately home in the fictional county of North Pimmshire, with their extended family: son and heir Hon Jon, daughter Serena, and grandchildren, Freddy and Daisy. The daily, Mrs Shagpile, and love of Dicky's life, Slobber, his black Labrador, and the latest addition to the family, Scribble, Daisy's working Cocker Spaniel, also make regular appearances.

Annie Tempest was born in Zambia in 1959. She has a huge international following and has had eighteen one-woman shows, from Mexico to Mayfair. Her work is now syndicated from New York to Dubai.

Calories are tiny little critters that live in cupboards and eat
bits off your waistbands at nights ...

DECEMBER – JANUARY

29 Monday

30 Tuesday

31 Wednesday

New Year's Eve

1 Thursday

New Year's Day
Holiday, UK, Republic of Ireland, Canada, USA,
Australia and New Zealand

2 Friday

Holiday, Scotland and New Zealand

3 Saturday

4 Sunday

JANUARY

5 Monday   *Full Moon*

6 Tuesday   *Epiphany*

7 Wednesday

8 Thursday

9 Friday

10 Saturday

11 Sunday

A personal trainer has the skills and experience to motivate clients to reach a fitness level appropriate for their body...

Every meal you make
Every bite you take
I'll be watching you ...

JANUARY

---
12 Monday

---
13 Tuesday   *Last Quarter*

---
14 Wednesday

---
15 Thursday

---
16 Friday

---
17 Saturday

---
18 Sunday

JANUARY

---

19 Monday   Holiday, USA (Martin Luther King Jnr Day)

---

20 Tuesday   *First Quarter*

---

21 Wednesday

---

22 Thursday

---

23 Friday

---

24 Saturday

---

25 Sunday

The weighty decision...

---

26 Monday   Holiday, Australia (Australia Day)

---

27 Tuesday   *First Quarter*

---

28 Wednesday

---

29 Thursday

---

30 Friday

---

31 Saturday

---

1 Sunday

FEBRUARY

2 Monday

3 Tuesday   *Full Moon*

4 Wednesday

5 Thursday

6 Friday   Accession of Queen Elizabeth II
                                                  Holiday, New Zealand (Waitangi Day)

7 Saturday

8 Sunday

THE ENGLISH WOMAN IN THE TOWN
It doesn't matter how I dress in town because nobody knows who I am...

THE ENGLISH WOMAN IN THE COUNTRY
It doesn't matter how I dress in the country because everyone knows who I am...

© Annie Tempest

FEBRUARY

9 Monday

10 Tuesday

11 Wednesday

12 Thursday

Last Quarter

13 Friday

14 Saturday

Valentine's Day

15 Sunday

FEBRUARY

16 Monday   Holiday, USA (Presidents' Day)

17 Tuesday   Shrove Tuesday

18 Wednesday   *New Moon*
Ash Wednesday

19 Thursday   Chinese New Year

20 Friday

21 Saturday

22 Sunday

FEBRUARY ~ MARCH

23 Monday

24 Tuesday

25 Wednesday
First Quarter

26 Thursday

27 Friday

28 Saturday

1 Sunday
St David's Day

MARCH

2 Monday

3 Tuesday

4 Wednesday

5 Thursday   *Full Moon*

6 Friday

7 Saturday

8 Sunday

Daffy's prayer:

Today's been long and I'm half dead
But just before I hit my bed
It would be really awfully kind
- But only if you wouldn't mind -
If you could grant a wee request
- Because, tonight, I need my rest -
While I'm asleep, my strength restoring
Stop the dogs and Dicky snoring...

MARCH

9 Monday   *Commonwealth Day*

10 Tuesday

11 Wednesday

12 Thursday

13 Friday   *Last Quarter*

14 Saturday

15 Sunday   Mother's Day, UK and Republic of Ireland

MARCH

16 Monday

17 Tuesday

St Patrick's Day
Holiday, Northern Ireland and Republic of Ireland

18 Wednesday

19 Thursday

20 Friday

New Moon
Vernal Equinox (Spring begins)

21 Saturday

22 Sunday

MARCH

23 Monday

24 Tuesday

25 Wednesday

26 Thursday

27 Friday   *First Quarter*

28 Saturday

29 Sunday   British Summer Time begins
                                                                      Palm Sunday

MARCH – APRIL

30 Monday

31 Tuesday

1 Wednesday

2 Thursday

Maundy Thursday

3 Friday

Good Friday
Holiday, UK, Canada, Australia and New Zealand

4 Saturday

Full Moon
Holiday, Australia (Easter Saturday)
First day of Passover (Pesach)

5 Sunday

Easter Sunday

"I did exercise once, but I had an allergic reaction: my skin flushed, my heart raced and I got all sweaty and out of breath..."

APRIL

6 Monday

7 Tuesday

8 Wednesday

9 Thursday

10 Friday

11 Saturday

12 Sunday

Last Quarter

APRIL

13 Monday

14 Tuesday

15 Wednesday

16 Thursday

17 Friday

18 Saturday

New Moon

19 Sunday

With age, you learn that pleasing everyone
is impossible...
Really annoying everyone, on the other hand,
is a piece of cake...

APRIL

20 Monday

21 Tuesday   Birthday of Queen Elizabeth II

22 Wednesday

23 Thursday   St George's Day

24 Friday

25 Saturday   *First Quarter*
                                                        Holiday, Australia (Anzac Day)

26 Sunday

27 Monday

Holiday, New Zealand (Anzac Day)

28 Tuesday

29 Wednesday

30 Thursday

1 Friday

2 Saturday

3 Sunday

Of course I remembered it was your birthday!

I've prepared a wonderful dentally friendly lunch al fresco for you...

Just remove the cork...

According to this BMI chart, I am too short...

4 Monday

Full Moon
Early Spring Holiday, UK
Holiday, Republic of Ireland

5 Tuesday

6 Wednesday

7 Thursday

8 Friday

9 Saturday

10 Sunday

Mother's Day, USA, Canada,
Australia and New Zealand

MAY

---

11 Monday   *Last Quarter*

---

12 Tuesday

---

13 Wednesday

---

14 Thursday   *Ascension Day*

---

15 Friday

---

16 Saturday

---

17 Sunday

The kids seem to be completely addicted to the internet...

...There must be something one can do about it, surely...

Oh! I know. I'll google it...

If a man says he'll do it – he will. No need to keep asking him every six months...

MAY

---

18 Monday

New Moon
Holiday, Canada (Victoria Day)

---

19 Tuesday

---

20 Wednesday

---

21 Thursday

---

22 Friday

---

23 Saturday

---

24 Sunday

Whit Sunday
Feast of Weeks (Shavuot)

MAY

25 Monday

First Quarter
Spring Bank Holiday, UK
Holiday, USA (Memorial Day)

26 Tuesday

27 Wednesday

28 Thursday

29 Friday

30 Saturday

31 Sunday

Trinity Sunday

Panel 1: The swallows are getting in and nesting in the Oak Room four poster again—can you deal with it?..

Panel 2: You men are all the same. You only hear what you want to hear...

Panel 3: Sorry, darling? Did you say lunch was ready?

JUNE

1 Monday

Holiday, Republic of Ireland
Holiday, New Zealand (The Queen's Birthday)

2 Tuesday

Full Moon
Coronation Day

3 Wednesday

4 Thursday

Corpus Christi

5 Friday

6 Saturday

7 Sunday

JUNE

---

8 Monday Holiday, Australia (The Queen's Birthday)

---

9 Tuesday *Last Quarter*

---

10 Wednesday

---

11 Thursday

---

12 Friday

---

13 Saturday The Queen's Official Birthday (subject to confirmation)

---

14 Sunday

Any messages, Mrs Shagpile?

Now you mention it, there was one from Lord Muddiegirth...

He rang to say he's got dementia seats at Twickenham...

"According to the henge we're in the middle of British summertime"

JUNE

15 Monday

16 Tuesday   *New Moon*

17 Wednesday

18 Thursday   First day of Ramadân

19 Friday

20 Saturday

21 Sunday   Summer Solstice (Summer begins)
                                  Father's Day, UK, Republic of Ireland,
                                  USA and Canada

JUNE

22 Monday

23 Tuesday

24 Wednesday   *First Quarter*

25 Thursday

26 Friday

27 Saturday

28 Sunday

" I'm trying to install summer but it says:
NOT VALID IN THE U.K... "

---

29 Monday

---

30 Tuesday

---

1 Wednesday   Holiday, Canada (Canada Day)

---

2 Thursday   *Full Moon*

---

3 Friday   Holiday, USA

---

4 Saturday   Independence Day, USA

---

5 Sunday

JULY

6 Monday

7 Tuesday

8 Wednesday *Last Quarter*

9 Thursday

10 Friday

11 Saturday

12 Sunday Battle of the Boyne

This one was a brave soldier who died in the war
IVOR SHAGPILE
RIP
...and this one was alive when Henry XIIIth was on the throne...
Annie Tempest © 2013
It's so interesting isn't it, Freddy! It's like a history lesson...
DIED BECAUSE HE DIDN'T FORWARD AN EMAIL TO 5 FRIENDS 2013
GLADYS MOPP loving wife of ERNIE MOPP died peacefully 1964
1924 - 1945 RIP

13 Monday

14 Tuesday

15 Wednesday
St Swithin's Day

16 Thursday
New Moon

17 Friday
Eid al-Fitr (end of Ramadân)

18 Saturday

19 Sunday

JULY

20 Monday

21 Tuesday

22 Wednesday

23 Thursday

24 Friday   *First Quarter*

25 Saturday

26 Sunday

THE IMPORTANCE OF GETTING THE WHOLE TAP ROOT...

27 Monday

28 Tuesday

29 Wednesday

30 Thursday

31 Friday

Full Moon

1 Saturday

2 Sunday

AUGUST

3 Monday

4 Tuesday

5 Wednesday

6 Thursday

7 Friday *Last Quarter*

8 Saturday

9 Sunday

'There are lane closures in both directions at South Pimms with traffic tailing back to Havock in the Wreake and Waddles End. Engineering work is disrupting First TransPimmshire trains on all routes with replacement bus services between Mugglesford and Rottingbeam...'

THE MALE CHARACTER: The strict adherence to her rules: No dog mud in the house...

AUGUST

10 Monday

11 Tuesday

12 Wednesday

13 Thursday

14 Friday   *New Moon*

15 Saturday

16 Sunday

AUGUST

17 Monday

18 Tuesday

19 Wednesday

20 Thursday

21 Friday

22 Saturday   *First Quarter*

23 Sunday

AUGUST

24 Monday

25 Tuesday

26 Wednesday

27 Thursday

28 Friday

29 Saturday   *Full Moon*

30 Sunday

AUGUST – SEPTEMBER

31 Monday   Holiday, UK (exc. Scotland)

1 Tuesday

2 Wednesday

3 Thursday

4 Friday

5 Saturday   Last Quarter

6 Sunday   Father's Day (Australia and New Zealand)

Finally the rain has stopped and we can get back into the garden and see what's what ...

Yes. I appear to have grown something rather unexpected over the winter this year...

Damned ornamental pond bolted and spread into a Bonsai Lake...

SEPTEMBER

7 Monday

8 Tuesday

9 Wednesday

10 Thursday

11 Friday

12 Saturday

13 Sunday

New Moon

SEPTEMBER

14 Monday   Jewish New Year (Rosh Hashanah)

15 Tuesday

16 Wednesday

17 Thursday

18 Friday

19 Saturday

20 Sunday

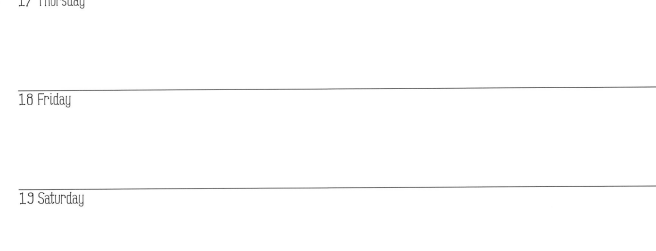

Lady Tottering,
Tottering Hall,
Tottering-by-Gently,
Rottingbeam,
N. Pimmshire

Tsk! You've got dippy egg on your good shirt! Come on! Grandpa's guest wants to meet you...

Shoulders back. Smile and shake hands nicely...

Look Granny. He's got his beard on backwards!

SEPTEMBER

21 Monday

First Quarter

22 Tuesday

23 Wednesday

Autumnal Equinox (Autumn begins)
Day of Atonement (Yom Kippur)

24 Thursday

25 Friday

26 Saturday

27 Sunday

SEPTEMBER - OCTOBER

---

28 Monday

Full Moon
First day of Tabernacles (Succoth)

---

29 Tuesday

Michaelmas Day

---

30 Wednesday

---

1 Thursday

---

2 Friday

---

3 Saturday

---

4 Sunday

Last Quarter

"I take it you enjoyed the Golf Dinner last night, dear..."

Come on, Inner Peace! I haven't got all day!

OCTOBER

5 Monday

6 Tuesday

7 Wednesday

8 Thursday

9 Friday

10 Saturday

11 Sunday

OCTOBER

12 Monday   Holiday, Canada (Thanksgiving)
                                             Holiday, USA (Columbus Day)

13 Tuesday   *New Moon*

14 Wednesday

15 Thursday   Islamic New Year

16 Friday

17 Saturday

18 Sunday

Panel 1: I can't remember who but someone told me recently that Ginseng was good for the memory...

Panel 2: It took me months to remember to buy some...

Panel 3: ...and I must have put it somewhere safe because I can't find it anywhere.

I don't think he even noticed...

OCTOBER

19 Monday

---

20 Tuesday   *First Quarter*

---

21 Wednesday

---

22 Thursday

---

23 Friday

---

24 Saturday

---

25 Sunday   British Summer Time ends

OCTOBER - NOVEMBER

26 Monday

Holiday, Republic of Ireland
Holiday, New Zealand (Labour Day)

27 Tuesday

Full Moon

28 Wednesday

29 Thursday

30 Friday

31 Saturday

Halloween

1 Sunday

All Saints' Day

It's fabulous having grey hair!

...just ask any bald man...

"No, darling—I can't invite the Crepuscula-Harflytes—there's far too much risk of being invited back...."

NOVEMBER

2 Monday

3 Tuesday   *Last Quarter*

4 Wednesday

5 Thursday   Guy Fawkes

6 Friday

7 Saturday

8 Sunday   Remembrance Sunday

NOVEMBER

9 Monday

10 Tuesday

11 Wednesday

New Moon
Holiday, USA (Veterans' Day))
Holiday, Canada (Remembrance Day))

12 Thursday

13 Friday

14 Saturday

15 Sunday

I have tried to shop in a cheaper super-market than Waitrose but I won't be doing that again...

Why? Was the food disgusting?

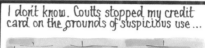

I don't know. Coutts stopped my credit card on the grounds of suspicious use...

I'm restricting myself to just one glass of wine a night now...
Anne Tempest ©2009

NOVEMBER

16 Monday

17 Tuesday

18 Wednesday

19 Thursday   *First Quarter*

20 Friday

21 Saturday

22 Sunday

NOVEMBER

23 Monday

24 Tuesday

25 Wednesday

Full Moon

26 Thursday

Holiday, USA (Thanksgiving

27 Friday

28 Saturday

29 Sunday

First Sunday in Adven

I'd like you to gold leaf all the embellishment on the white drawing room ceiling and have the Gillow re-upholstered...

...and while you're at it, redecorate the billiard room.. oh, yes, and re-lead the west wing roof...

Come down off the mantelpiece, Dicky, you're having one of your 19th Century pre-taxation dreams...

NOVEMBER – DECEMBER

30 Monday   *St Andrew's Day*

1 Tuesday

2 Wednesday

3 Thursday   *Last Quarter*

4 Friday

5 Saturday

6 Sunday   *Hannukah begins*

DECEMBER

---

7 Monday

---

8 Tuesday

---

9 Wednesday

---

10 Thursday

---

11 Friday   *New Moon*

---

12 Saturday

---

13 Sunday

Which one of those brain eroding social websites are you on now, Freddy? YouTube? Twitter? Facebook?
Or have they all merged into one super sized time wasting forum...?
'You twit Face...'
©2012

On school run this morning Jack said to me: "Mummy, when I grow up I want to be a man.":

Ah! Bless him! That's SOOoo sweet!

I know! He really thinks he can do both...

DECEMBER

14 Monday

15 Tuesday

16 Wednesday

17 Thursday

18 Friday
First Quarter

19 Saturday

20 Sunday

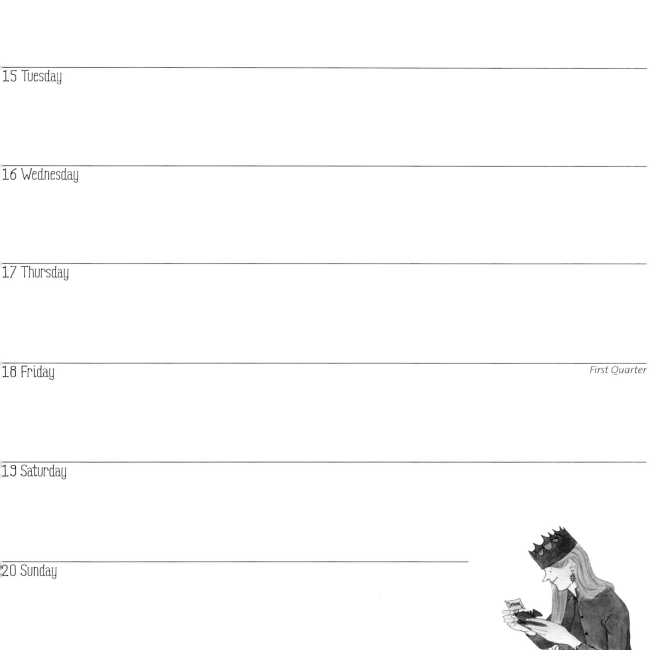

DECEMBER

21 Monday

22 Tuesday   Winter Solstice (Winter begins)

23 Wednesday

24 Thursday   Christmas Eve

25 Friday   *Full Moon*
                                                                  Christmas Day
                                      Holiday, UK, Republic of Ireland, USA, Canada,
                                                         Australia and New Zealand

26 Saturday   Boxing Day (St Stephen's Day)

27 Sunday

"HO HO HO ..."

HAPPY christmas

DECEMBER - JANUARY 2016

28 Monday — Holiday, UK, Republic of Ireland, Canada, Australia and New Zealand

29 Tuesday

30 Wednesday

31 Thursday — New Year's Eve

1 Friday — New Year's Day
Holiday, UK, Republic of Ireland, USA, Canada, Australia and New Zealand

2 Saturday

3 Sunday

NOTES